HARD-FI
ONCE UPON A TIME IN THE WEST

Published by
Wise Publications
14-15 Berners Street, London, W1T 3LJ, UK.

Exclusive distributors:
Music Sales Limited
Distribution Centre, Newmarket Road,
Bury St Edmunds, Suffolk, IP33 3YB, UK.

Music Sales Pty Limited
120 Rothschild Avenue, Rosebery,
NSW 2018, Australia.

Order No. AM992277
ISBN 978-1-84772-382-6
This book © Copyright 2007 Wise Publications,
a division of Music Sales Limited.

Edited by Fiona Bolton.
Music arranged by Derek Jones.
Music processed by Paul Ewers Music Design.

Printed in the EU.

Wise Publications
part of The Music Sales Group
London / New York / Paris / Sydney / Copenhagen / Berlin / Madrid / Tokyo

SUBURBAN KNIGHTS

Words & Music by Richard Archer

TONIGHT

Words & Music by Richard Archer

to - night,   to - night,   to - night,   to - night,   to - night,   to - night.

Oh.____   Oh.____

_____ *Instrumental ad lib.*

1, 2.   3.

I SHALL OVERCOME

Words & Music by Richard Archer

15

one, will come_ un - done." And I know I shall o - ver - come.

WATCH ME FALL APART

Words & Music by Richard Archer

smil - ing__ face   just brings   you down,   just brings_____ you down.

2. You let it   slip,   so get a   grip.   There's no - one

(3.) all,   all I could take.   I want - ed

else   to blame   for   this.   Now walk a - round   this lone -

ev - 'ry - thing__ my   way.   Thought I can't lose,   thought I was

- ly town,   where ev - 'ry   smil - ing__ face   just brings   you down,   just brings

smart.   And then that   girl   turned round   and broke   my heart,   and broke

I CLOSE MY EYES

Words & Music by Richard Archer

TELEVISION

Words & Music by Richard Archer

Life means noth-ing when no-one knows your name. I've nev-er had too much but I'd

give it all for fame. Ba - by, ba - by.

She's there on the T. V., so beau - ti - ful on screen,

sell - ing me a life I've nev - er known and nev - er seen. Ba - by,

ba - by. If I on - ly had

29

31

HELP ME PLEASE

Words & Music by Richard Archer

1. There's no light in the hall. There's no sound here at all.
2. Break-ing down on the stairs. Hel-lo lone-li-ness,

hel-lo des-pair. Emp-ti-ness, emp-ti-ness rules.
All of this, all of it's wrong.

'Cause be-ing a-lone___ scares the life___ out of me.

Be-ing a-lone___ scares the life___ out of

me.

me.

Be-ing a-lone___ scares the life___ out of me.

CAN'T GET ALONG (WITHOUT YOU)

Words & Music by Richard Archer

WE NEED LOVE

Words & Music by Richard Archer

LITTLE ANGEL

Words & Music by Richard Archer

1. When I'm

lone- ly___ deep in the cit- y at___ night,___ no-bod- y near___ me 'cept that
(2.) riv- er,___ yeah, it's a hun-dred miles___ wide.___ I can't see___ how I'll make___

red ne - on_____ light. I get down on my knees and I pray.__
___ the oth - er side. I get down, down on my knees and I pray.__

There you are dar - ling, bring sal - va - tion to - day. A shin - ing light, you
There you are dar - ling, sail - ing my way.

taste just right. I'm hun - gry, you feed me, keep watch - ing o - ver me 'cause dar - ling

you're my_____ oh, my lit - tle an - gel._____

Yeah, dar-ling you're my,_____ my lit - tle

an - gel._____ Whoa, whoa,_ whoa, whoa. 2. Come to a

Whoa, whoa,_ whoa,_ whoa.
I get a feel - ing.___ yeah, it's a mat-ter of___ fact.___ I'm

THE KING

Words & Music by Richard Archer